THE ADVENTURES OF K9
AND OTHER MECHANICAL CREATURES

THE ADVENTURES OF

AND OTHER MECHANICAL CREATURES

TERRANCE DICKS

A TARGET BOOK
published by
The Paperback Division of
W. H. Allen & Co. Ltd

A Target Book
Published in 1979
by the Paperback Division of W. H. Allen & Co. Ltd.
A Howard & Wyndham Company
44 Hill Street, London W1X 8LB.

Cover illustration by Andrew Skilleter
Illustrations by Andrew Skilleter

Printed in Great Britain by
Richard Clay (The Chaucer Press) Ltd
Bungay, Suffolk

ISBN 0 426 20067 5

We should like to thank the Doctor Who Appreciation Society,
and in particular the society's historian, Mr Jeremy Bentham,
for help in the preparation of this book.

CONTENTS

Hello!

This is the Doctor.

Here's a book all about my faithful friend, K9. As you know, K9 is a kind of robot dog – though he'd sooner be described as a completely-mobile, self-powered computer with multi-sensory circuits and built-in defensive capabilities.

K9 has been my faithful companion on many adventures, saving my life quite a few times, so I think he deserves a book of his own.

I'll also be telling you about some other amazing mechanical creatures I've encountered on my travels through Space and Time, some surprisingly friendly, others very dangerous indeed.

'Commence read-out programme, Master!'

K9's impatient to begin. He doesn't mind sharing a book, just as long as *he's* first. For an automaton, he's got a very well developed sense of his own importance!

On with the book then – and now it's time to meet that incredibly brave, enormously intelligent, handsome, faithful, versatile, mobile computer – K9! There, is *that* good enough?

'Affirmative, Master!'

7

K9'S PEDIGREE

There would never have been a K9 at all, if Professor Marius of New Heidelberg University hadn't been such a keen animal lover.

The Professor accepted a job at the Bi-Al Foundation, a combination space hospital and research centre way out in the asteroid belt. This was in 5,000 AD, when you humans will be just starting to make your first great leap across the galaxy. The Foundation was right on the

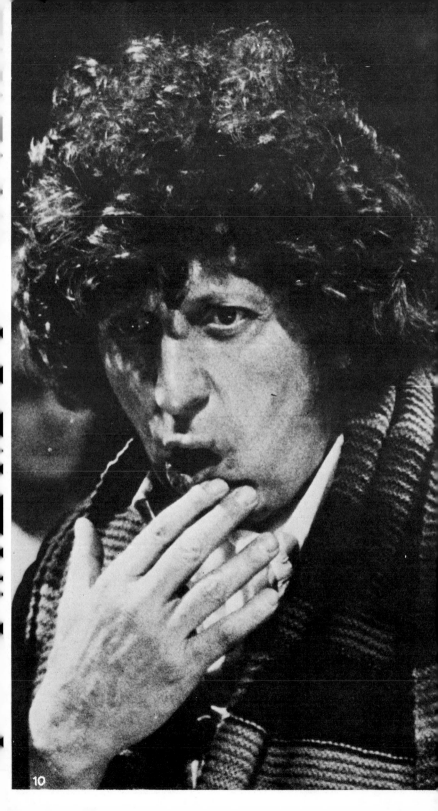

edge of your solar system, a good place to study the new diseases and dangers Man was sure to meet in space.

It was an interesting and exciting job, and the Professor was very happy – except for just one thing. He missed his dog. Weight restrictions on space travellers are very strict. Everything shipped out into space has to have a clear scientific purpose – and that doesn't include pets. Professor Marius just had to leave his dog behind with friends. He knew the dog would be well cared for – but he still missed him.

However, the Professor was a resourceful chap, and he soon found a solution. He asked the Foundation authorities for permission to design and construct a mobile computer unit to help in his research work.

Permission was granted – and then, of course, there was nothing to stop Professor Marius from building his computer in the shape of a robot dog. He even managed to give it some of the character of his pet back on Earth.

Although the result turned out to be *very* dog-like indeed, in both appearance and behaviour it was very much more than just a robot dog.

K9 can move, talk, perform all the functions of the most complicated computer – and he can defend himself as well. After all, not every dog has a built in photon blaster in his nose!

K9'S TRAVELS

I first met K9 during the adventure of
'*The Invisible Enemy*' which was a very nasty,
highly intelligent Virus, with plans to take
over the galaxy using humans for hosts.

Unfortunately, I became infected myself,
and Leela took me to the Bi-Al
Foundation for treatment.

K9 helped Professor Marius to find a
cure – and helped Leela to fight off the
human servants of the Virus at the same
time.

When the monster Virus had finally
been disposed of, and Leela and I were
about to go on our way, Professor Marius
asked if we'd like to take K9 with us.
The Professor was due to go back to
Earth soon, and he knew he'd run up
against the same old weight-restriction
problem. He wouldn't be allowed to take
his new pet back with him.

I was a bit dubious at first, but Leela
was very keen – and as for K9, he was
inside the TARDIS before I could turn
round.

Now it looks as if K9 is here to stay. I
must admit he often comes in very useful.
Mind you, he can be a bit of a nuisance
at times – he's very argumentative! But all
in all, I suppose I'm getting used to
him . . .

'*Likewise – Master!*'

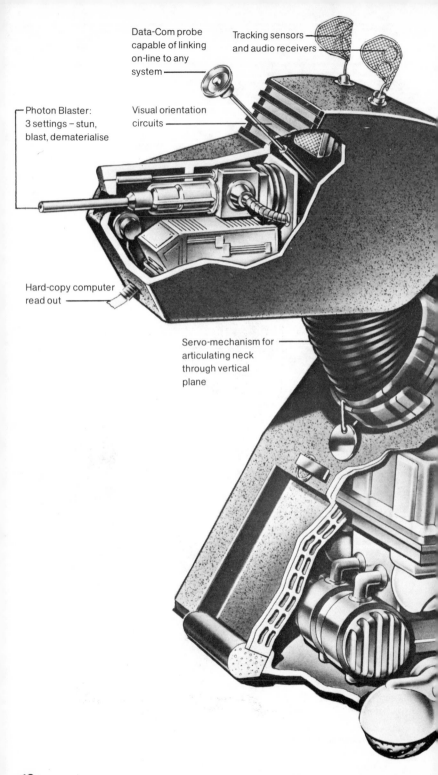

Data-Com probe
capable of linking
on-line to any
system

Tracking sensors
and audio receivers

Photon Blaster:
3 settings – stun,
blast, dematerialise

Visual orientation
circuits

Hard-copy computer
read out

Servo-mechanism for
articulating neck
through vertical
plane

16

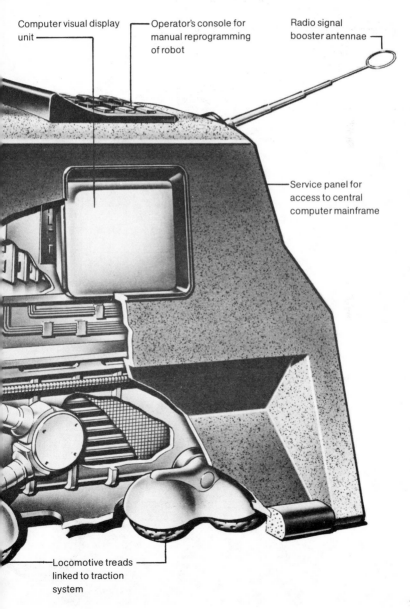

Computer visual display unit

Operator's console for manual reprogramming of robot

Radio signal booster antennae

Service panel for access to central computer mainframe

Locomotive treads linked to traction system

17

A touch of corrosion in his circuits kept K9 out of action for a while, but I had him nicely back in working order by the time we met 'The Sun Makers'.

A rascally organisation calling itself the Company had made Pluto habitable by adding an oxygen atmosphere and several powerful artificial suns. Now they were

working enslaved colonists to death, to
swell the Company profits.

K9 helped me to deal with that little
lot – and saved Leela from a very nasty
death by 'public steaming'. A good job
she was so keen for him to come with us!
'The Quest is the Quest!' That's what
these Minyan spacemen are always saying.
Small wonder their quest lasted for a
hundred thousand years!

They were searching for the P7E,
another Minyan space ship lost after their
planet had been destroyed. The lost ship
carried the Minyan race bank, and the
entire Minyan future depended on its
being found.

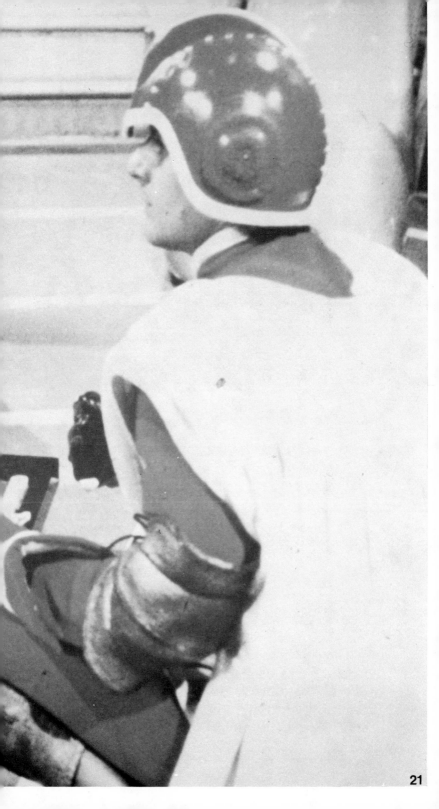

That's where K9 came in useful. His tracking capabilities helped to find the P7E. Unfortunately, it was now at the centre of a newly-formed planet on the very edge of creation.

The adventure that followed took us all
into strange and sinister 'Underworld' –
and K9's weaponry came in very useful in
getting us out again!

1

2

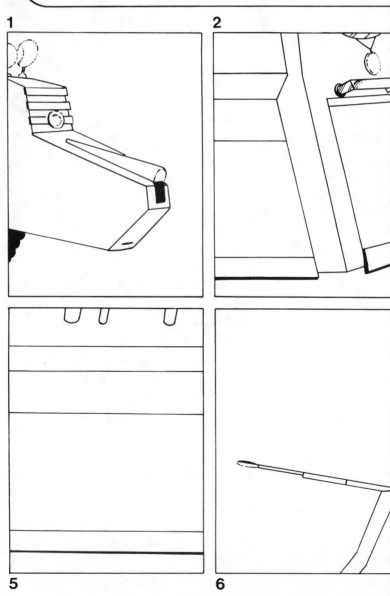

24 **5**

6

K9 is out of sequence. Can you put him
together? See the end of the book for the answers.

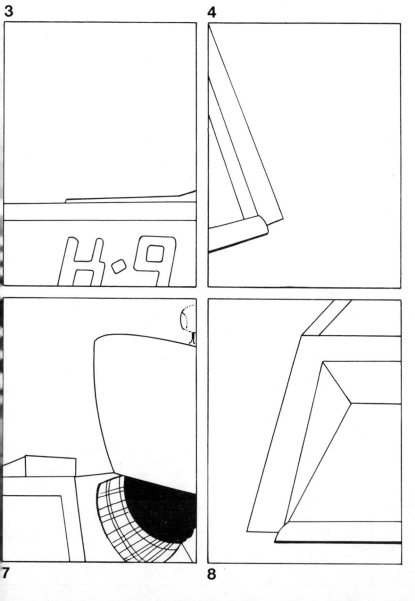

3

4

7

8

A desperate situation for K9. He has to defuse this giant computerised bomb quickly before it explodes. Can you help? He has to neutralise the row of lower connections in strict order as they are numbered along the top. The problem is that the connections are not in order on the lower line. To help you and K9. F is connection number 1. The other answers are at the end of the book.

'*The Invasion of Time*' was a baffling business indeed, and if Leela and K9 thought I was acting strangely for a time – well, they had good reason.

I was trying to foil an invasion of my home planet, Gallifrey, by the Vardans who were helping some of my oldest and most determined enemies, the Sontarans.

Fiercely militaristic, the Sontarans are a cunning and determined foe, and I had to use even greater cunning to defeat them, pretending to betray Gallifrey in order to save it.

K9 and Leela tried valiantly to help me, though they didn't know what I was up to half the time. Here's K9 having a spot of bother with the Commander of the Capitol Guard . . .

I left one companion on Gallifrey – Leela decided to stay behind with Andred, Commander of the Capitol Guard. In a way I lost two. K9 decided to stay with them.

But only in a way. Luckily I had a spare set of blueprints, and soon K9, Mark II, was in full operation. He was the old K9 all over again – with one or two little extras. Improved tracking circuits, more durable power-source, a new multi-phase blaster . . . I love a bit of tinkering, and I couldn't resist making a few improvements.

Before very long, a summons from the White Guardian, one of the two Guardians of Time, got me mixed up in '*The Ribos Operation*', first of a whole new series of adventures. I was given the task of finding the six segments of the Key to Time, in order to save the universe from chaos.

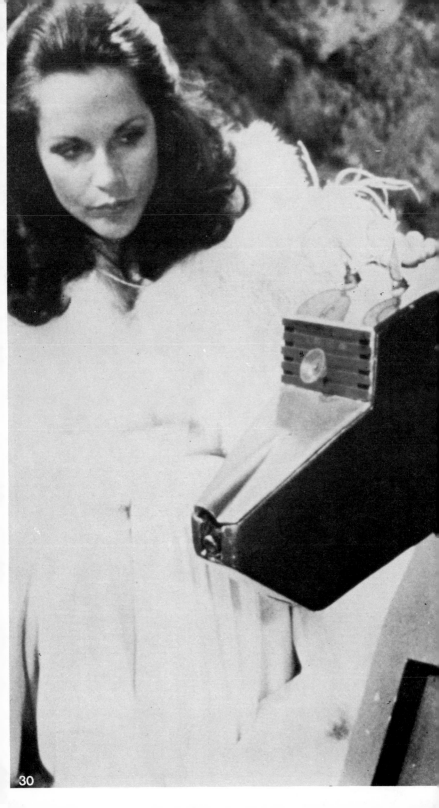

I was given a new companion to help me, a Time Lady called Romana. Here she is having a little chat with K9. Luckily, they get on very well together . . . K9 always seems to make a hit with the ladies.

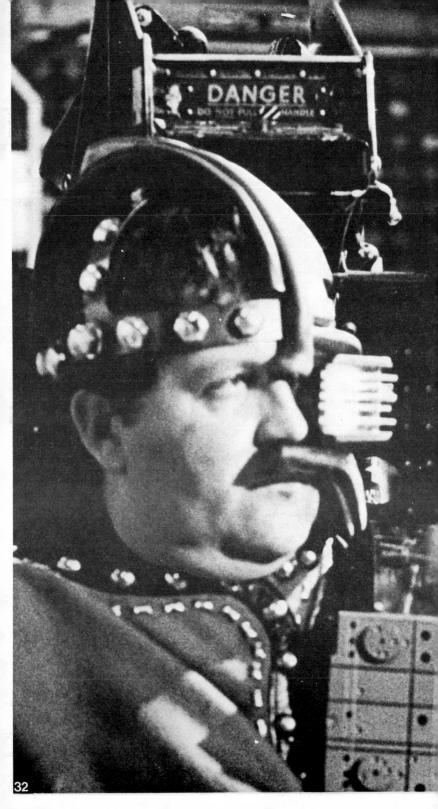

DANGER
DO NOT PULL HANDLE

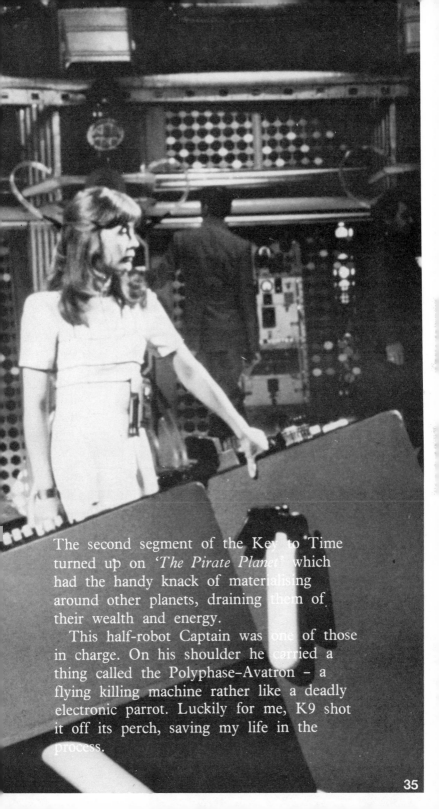

The second segment of the Key to Time turned up on *The Pirate Planet* which had the handy knack of materialising around other planets, draining them of their wealth and energy.

This half-robot Captain was one of those in charge. On his shoulder he carried a thing called the Polyphase–Avatron – a flying killing machine rather like a deadly electronic parrot. Luckily for me, K9 shot it off its perch, saving my life in the process.

Help Dr Who find his way through the maze.
Shade in his path. Do not cross over lines or
double back and all will be revealed!

On his travels Dr Who has come across these space vehicles. He wonders if you know their names and if you can say if they are manned or unmanned?
The answers are at the end of the book.

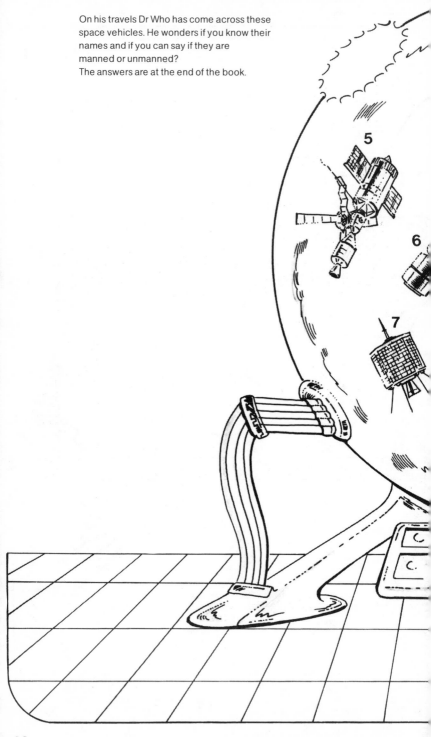

Back on Earth, we ran into '*The Stones of Blood*'. This mini-Stonehenge was the lair of creatures called Ogri, terrifying alien monsters who feed on blood.

A fierce-looking lady is their mistress, a very unpleasant alien criminal called Cessair of Diplos.

K9 held the fort valiantly while I tried to find Romana, who was held captive on a mysterious prison-ship orbitting the Earth in hyper-space.

I built this rather splendid hyper-space projector so that I could follow and rescue her. It worked very well – for a time!

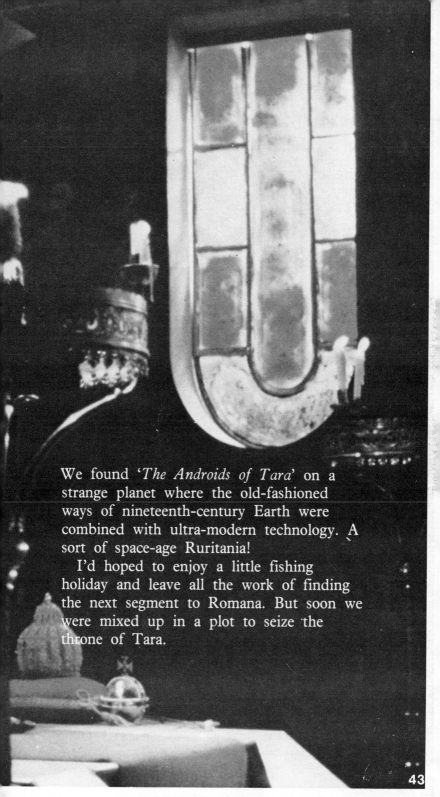

We found *'The Androids of Tara'* on a strange planet where the old-fashioned ways of nineteenth-century Earth were combined with ultra-modern technology. A sort of space-age Ruritania!

I'd hoped to enjoy a little fishing holiday and leave all the work of finding the next segment to Romana. But soon we were mixed up in a plot to seize the throne of Tara.

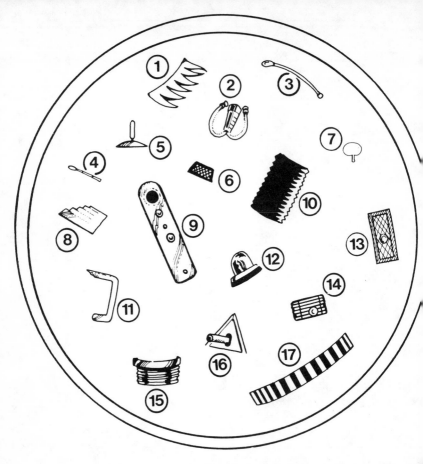

K9 and some of the other mechanical marvels have l[ost]
a few parts. Put them together again.
The answers are at the end of the book.

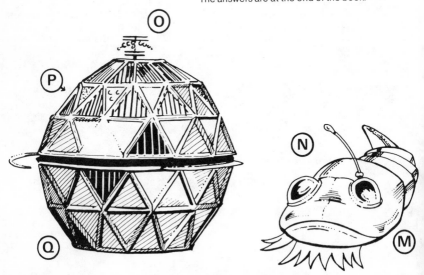

45

The Tardis is travelling through our Solar system.
Dr Who wonders if you can answer these questions?
The answers are at the end of the book.

A. Which planet is 1200 times larger than the earth?
B. Where did man make his first soft-landing of a space probe?
C. Which planet has triple 'rings'?
D. One planet is named after a sea god. Which?
E. In early times man new only of five planets in the
    Solar system then in 1781 a sixth was discovered.
    Which?

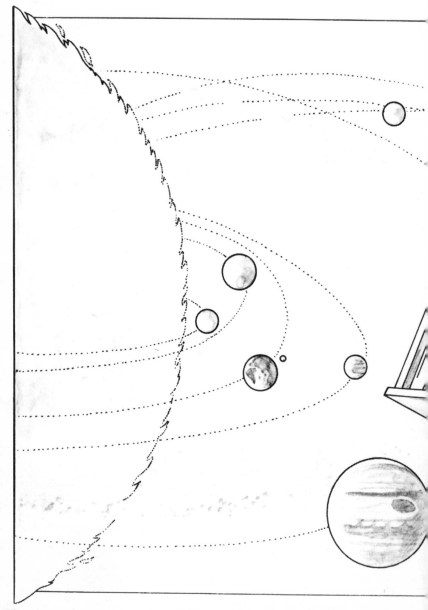

F. Only one natural satellite has been conquered by man.
   Do you know which?
G. Which is the smallest inner planet?
H. Perhaps these are the result of a gigantic collision of planets?
I. This three quarters of this planet's surface is covered
   by water.
J. One planet in the Solar system goes around the sun
   in a different way to all the others. Which one?
K. Does life exist on other planets? If it does earth
   scientists think that this planet is most likely to be the one.
L. There is only one star in the Earth's Solar system.
   What do we call it?

In fact, what with android doubles and human doubles all over the place, we were pretty mixed up altogether.

That's where K9's sensors came in useful. He was often the only one who could tell who was human and who a robot copy.

K9 was in dock again while we were fighting 'The Power of Kroll'. Just as well really, since it all happened on a soggy, swampy planet – the poor old chap would probably have gone rusty!

By the time K9 was himself again, only one segment had to be found.

K9 played a valiant part in the adventure called 'The Armageddon Factor', helping to defeat the warlike Marshal and his even more sinister Master, the Shadow.

This time K9 had a narrow escape himself! The Marshal actually tried to melt him down for scrap! K9 on the junk-pile – I ask you!

MAKE YOUR OWN K9

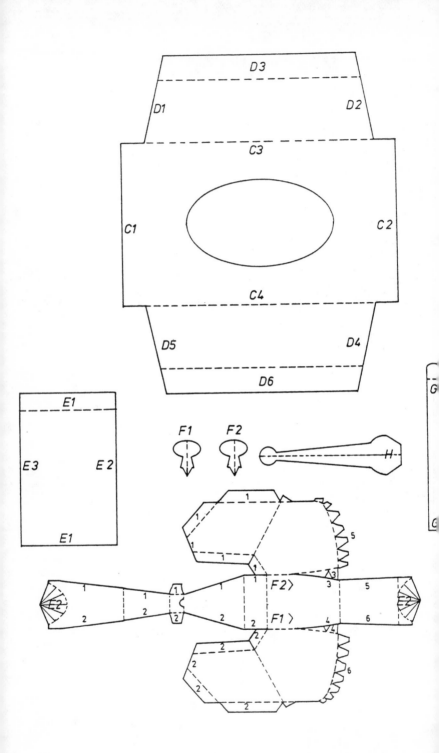

50

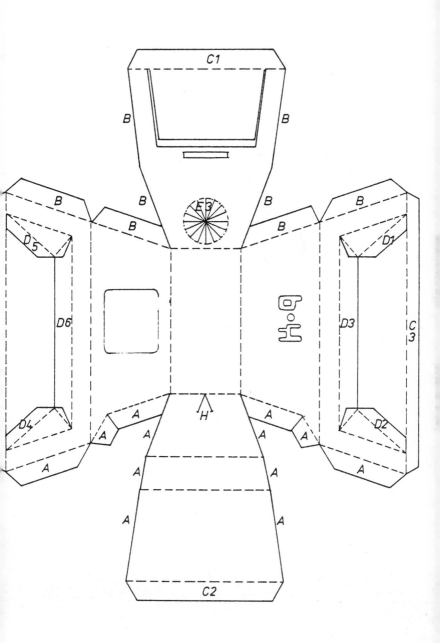

INSTRUCTIONS

BODY 1 Cut along the solid lines and score the dashed
lines. Then glue the tabs B at the front to their
opposite B edges, and glue the A tabs to the A
edges at the back. Fold all the D panels inwards.

BASE 2 Cut, score and fold as shown in the diagram.
Then push the two side panels (D 1-2-3) and (D 4-5-6)
into the D area in the body. All numbered positions
should be glued to the appropriate number on the body.

HEAD This should be cut out, scored, then glued in
number order as with the body.

NECK This is a tube joined by gluing E1 to E1. Some
glue can be placed on the E3 edge, then this can be
glued into the E3 hole in the body.
The collar is made by gluing G to G and is slipped
over the neck.
Then the E2 edge (with a little glue) is pushed
through the E2 hole under the head.

EARS The ears are slightly folded along their central
creases and glued into the F1 and F2 V-shaped
slots in the head.

TAIL This is folded along the central crease and glued
in the V-shaped slot àt H.

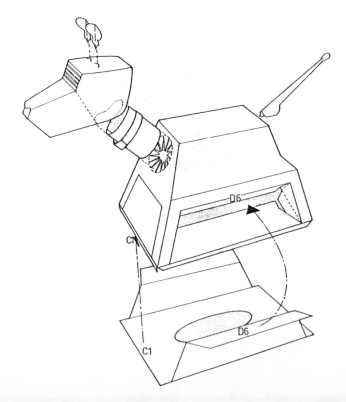

SOME OTHER MECHANICAL MARVELS!

Not all my mechanical acquaintances are as lovable as K9. In a highly technological galaxy, I've met quite a few machine-like creatures. Some have been friendly, some very much the opposite . . .

Doesn't this Mechanoid look friendly!

The Mechanoids
A robot race, originally sent to prepare the planet Mechanus for colonisation. But the colonists never arrived, and the Mechanoids become rulers of the planet.

Ice Soldiers
These were the robot guardians of one of the keys to the Conscience of Marinus, programmed to kill all those who didn't use the proper access-codes.

Robomen
'Robotised' human captives, programmed to serve their Dalek masters. The process always ended in the destruction of the human subjects – a typical Dalek scheme.

Chumblies
Robot servants of the ugly but highly-civilised Rills. Although armed with a deadly laser beam, the Chumblies were forbidden to kill by the orders of their pacifist masters. Nice to meet a peaceful robot for a change!

Fancy one of these for your next school outing?

59

No one looks very happy with the
Chumblies here!

Two of these Mechanoids carry special instructions for Doctor Who. They are identical but different in one small detail from the other Mechanoids. Can you spot which they are? The answer is at the end of the book.

63

War Machines

WOTAN, the super-computer installed in the Post Office Tower, decided that *it* was the destined ruler of Earth, and created War Machines to carry out its plan of conquest. Surprising how often computers get carried away with their own importance!

Cybermen

Once humanoid, these creatures from the planet Mondas replaced more and more of their bodies with bionic parts. In the end they became more robot than human, losing all emotion, obedient only to their own icy logic.

The *Cybermats* were their rat-like servant-creatures with a number of deadly skills in attack and sabotage. Rat poison was no use – but gold-dust finished them off!

A

D

E

G

H

K

The Tardis is a very advanced form of transport.
Dr Who wonders if you know about earlier forms of
transport. Can you put these into their correct
sequence from earliest times to today?
The answers are at the end of the book.

This is Cybermen weather!

Here is an abandoned space craft Doctor
Who is exploring. Its all very puzzling because some
of the objects here would not be of use.
As you know in space there would be no
gravity! Do you know which of these items are useless?
The answers are at the end of the book.

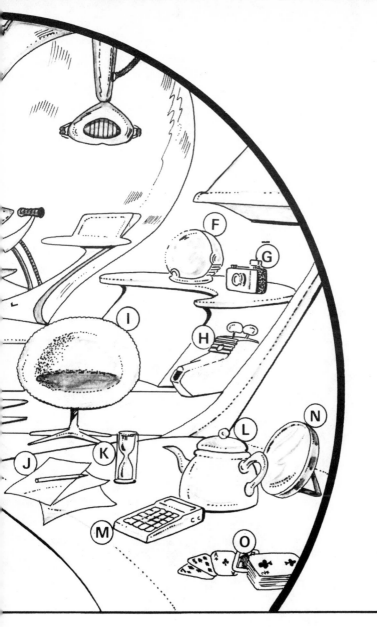

A Fixed lamp   E Pipe   I Easy chair   M Calculator

B Glass of water   F Space helmet   J Paper & pencil   N Mirror

C Dr Who's hat   G Camera   K Egg timer   O Playing cards

D Record player   H K9   L Teapot   P Weights

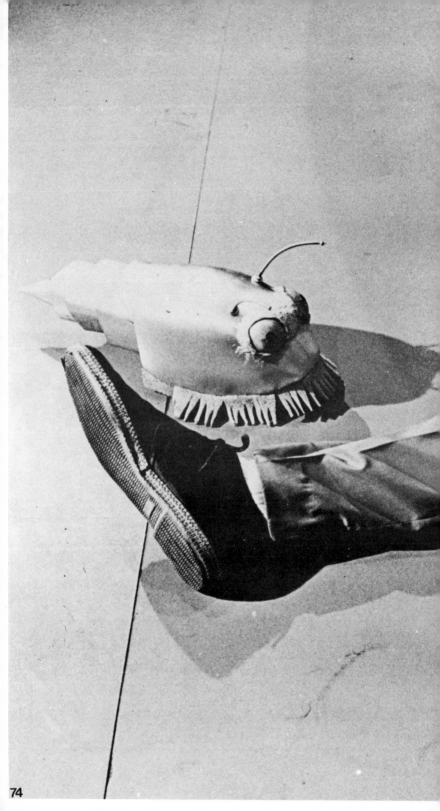

Who said Cybermats were cuddly?

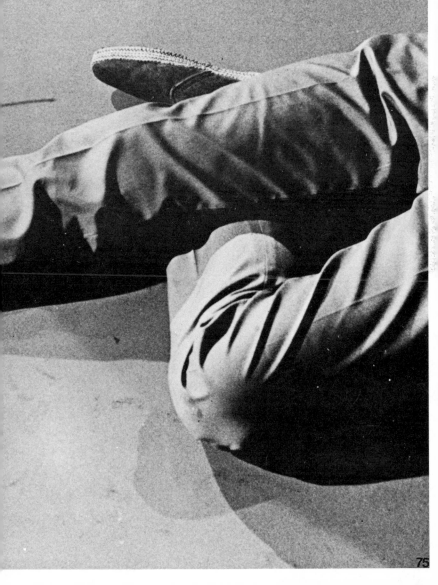

Fancy one of these as a pet?

When the Giant Robot grew
in size we had these drawings
made. Can you put them in
their correct order?
Look at the end of the
book for the answer.

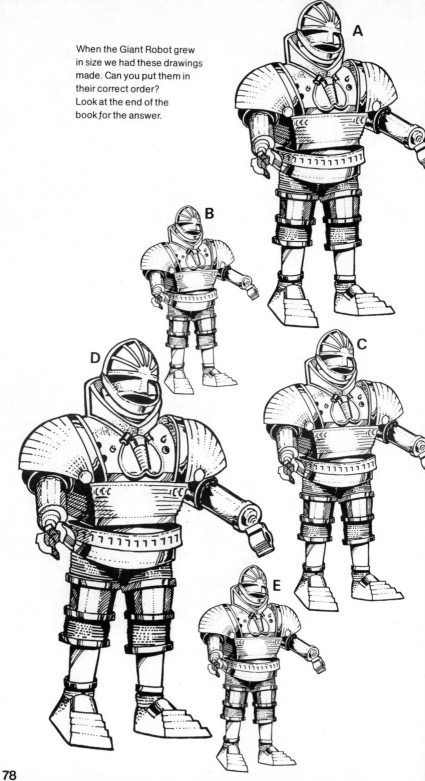

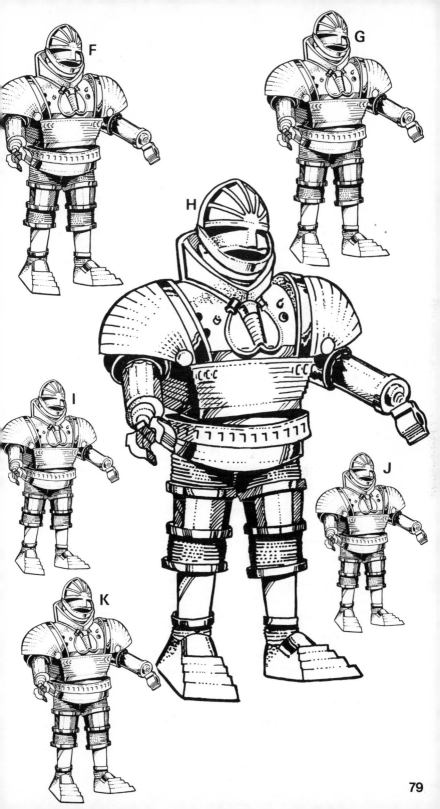

Yeti
Despite their furry, animal-like appearance, the Yeti were really robots, created in the form of 'abominable snowmen' by a formless alien intelligence with plans to conquer Earth. Not nearly as cuddly as they looked, the Yeti!

The Quarks
Small atomic-powered robots with high-pitched voices, the Quarks were the servants of the ruthless Dominators. Little and nasty, that sums up the Quarks.

The White Robots and the Clockwork Soldiers
Servants of the Master Computer which controlled a fairy-tale world of fiction. Its ruler actually wanted me to take his place!

The Krotons
More crystalline rather than mechanical, the Krotons depended for survival on mental energy stolen from others. No wonder they were after my brain!

Ah, one of our charming Autons!

The Autons

Again, not really mechanical, the Nestenes were energy-creatures with a liking for plastic, which they could bring to life, creating a wide variety of deadly and deceptive shapes. You never knew with Nestenes – anything from a doll to a daffodil could be a killer.

Arcturus

Really a living creature, Arcturus needed this mechanical life-support system to survive on the planet Peladon. The system included hearing and speech circuits, and a laser-weapon. Unfortunately, Arcturus was just as nasty as he looked!

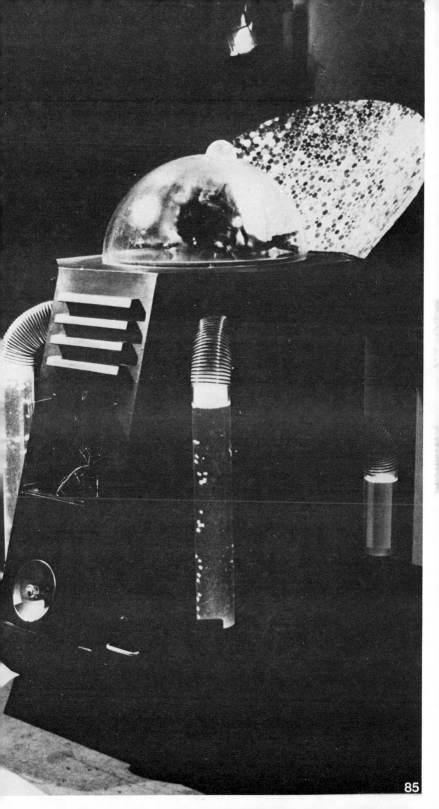

Robot Knight

Created by my old friend, the Sontaran Linx, this fighting robot looked like a knight in armour. Unkillable and unstoppable, it was a deadly but erratic weapon, as its owner found out when it turned on him!

Giant Robot

Made to replace Man in the difficult and dangerous task of space exploration, the Robot was seized and misused by some very unpleasant scientists. It went berserk, grew to enormous size, and at last I had to destroy it. Sarah was very upset, I remember.

Steyre's Robot

Servant of another Sontaran, this robot's job was to seek out and capture human prisoners, tying them up with flexible steel cords.

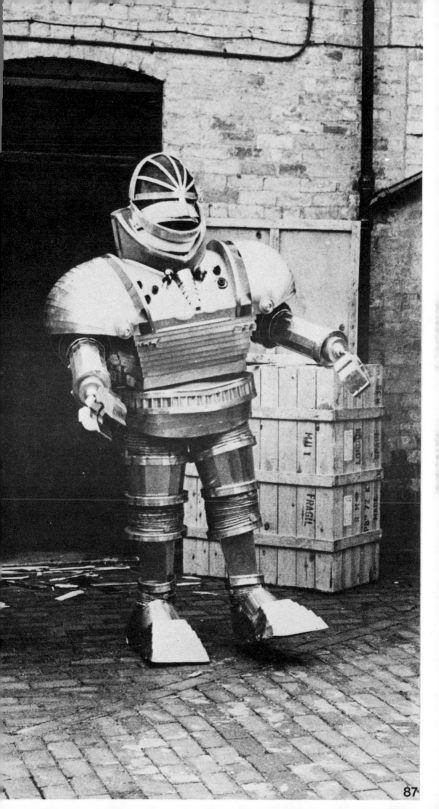

Doctor Who is on the trail of some
of his mechanical enemies and has come across their
tracks. The problem is he is not quite sure which
track belongs to which monster. Can you help him?
Put the number of each monster against the letter
given for each track. You can check your answer
at the end of the book.

89

The Mummies

Immensely strong and powerful, these were the servo-robots of the Osirians, an alien race who ruled for a time over Ancient Egypt. They were given this shape to terrify the Osirian's human servants, and they could give you a very nasty squeeze if they got their hands on you.

Kraal Androids

Highly convincing copies of human beings, these androids were the secret weapons of the Kraals in a well-planned invasion of Earth. They even had the cheek to copy me!

Voc Robots

The Vocs and their non-speaking inferiors, the Dums, did all the hard work on the totally robot-dependent society that produced the Sandminer. One of them wasn't nearly as Dum as he looked!

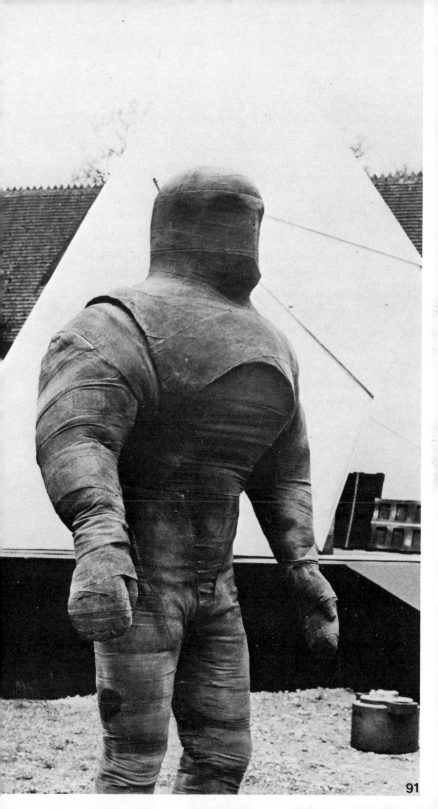

The Polyphase Avatron
This flying killing machine enabled the Captain of the Pirate Planet to terrorise his subordinates. Luckily K9 managed to shoot it down!

The Androids of Tara
Like the Kraal androids, these were basically replicas of existing humans – though K9 at least could always tell the real thing from the copy!

Servo-Robot
I met this robot in an abandoned space rocket. It was only trying to do its job – but it nearly disposed of me and my companions in the process!

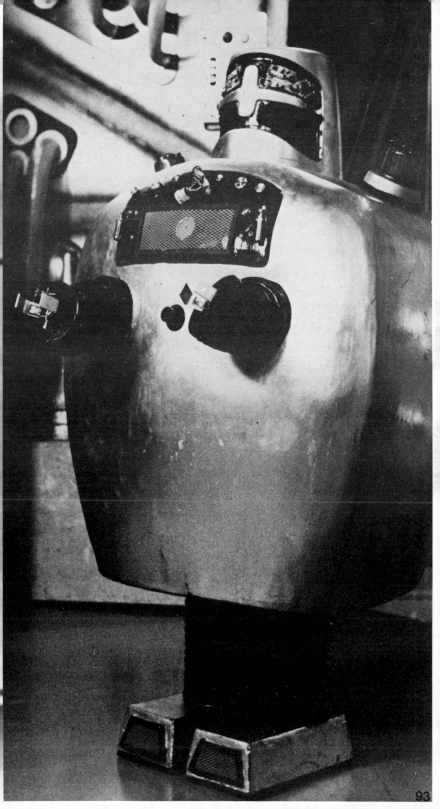

QUIZ ANSWERS

P 24 *Out of Sequence*
6,3,7,1
8,5,2,4

P 26 *Defuse the Bomb*
1.F, 2.C, 3.H, 4.G, 5.I, 6.B, 7.E, 8.J, 9.A, 10.D

P 38 *A Space Puzzle*
1. Skylab (m) 2. Mercury capsule (m) 3. Soyuz (m)
4. Intelsat IV 5. Tardis (m) 6. Sputnik I
7. Early Bird (USA) 8. Lunar train (m) 9. Telstar
10. Mariner

P44 *Mysterious Parts*
A.4, B.7, C.17, D.2, E.14, F.8, G.11, H.9, I.12, J.13,
K.10, L.6

P 46 *A Solar Puzzle*
A. Jupiter B. Venus C. Saturn D. Neptune
E. Uranus F. The Moon G. Mercury
H. The Asteroids situated between Mars and
Jupiter I. The Earth J. Pluto K. Mars L. The Sun

P 62 *Spot the Mechanoid Difference*
D, J

P66 *A Tardis Puzzle*
1.F, 2.G, 3.D, 4.J, 5.B, 6.I, 7.E, 8.C, 9.H, 10.K

P72 *Gravity Puzzle*
B, C, D, E, I, J, K, L, O, P,

P 78 *The Giant Robot*
1.H, 2.D, 3.A, 4.C, 5.F, 6.G, 7.K, 8.E, 9.J, 10.I, 11.B

P 88 *A Trail Problem*
1.A, 2.C, 3.F, 4.B, 5.D, 6.E

'Doctor Who'

Δ	0426114558	Terrance Dicks **DOCTOR WHO AND THE ABOMINABLE SNOWMEN**	70p
Δ	0426200373	Terrance Dicks **DOCTOR WHO AND THE ANDROID INVASION**	60p
Δ	0426116313	Ian Marter **DOCTOR WHO AND THE ARK IN SPACE**	70p
Δ	0426116747	Terrance Dicks **DOCTOR WHO AND THE BRAIN OF MORBIUS**	60p
Δ	0426110250	Terrance Dicks **DOCTOR WHO AND THE CARNIVAL OF MONSTERS**	70p
Δ	042611471X	Malcolm Hulke **DOCTOR WHO AND THE CAVE-MONSTERS**	70p
Δ	0426117034	Terrance Dicks **DOCTOR WHO AND THE CLAWS OF AXOS**	70p
Δ	0426113160	David Whitaker **DOCTOR WHO AND THE CRUSADERS**	70p
Δ	0426114981	Brian Hayles **DOCTOR WHO AND THE CURSE OF PELADON**	70p
Δ	042611244X	Terrance Dicks **DOCTOR WHO AND THE DALEK INVASION OF EARTH**	70p
Δ	0426103807	Terrance Dicks **DOCTOR WHO AND THE DAY OF THE DALEKS**	70p
Δ	0426101103	David Whitaker **DOCTOR WHO AND THE DALEKS**	70p
Δ	0426119657	Terrance Dicks **DOCTOR WHO AND THE DEADLY ASSASSIN**	60p
Δ	0426200063	Terrance Dicks **DOCTOR WHO AND THE FACE OF EVIL**	70p
Δ	0426112601	Terrance Dicks **DOCTOR WHO AND THE GENESIS OF THE DALEKS**	60p

† For sale in Britain and Ireland only.
* Not for sale in Canada.
♦ Film & T.V. tie-ins.

If you enjoyed this book and would like to have information sent to you about other TARGET titles, write to the address below.

You will also receive:
A FREE TARGET BADGE!
Based on the TARGET BOOKS symbol — see front cover of this book — this attractive three-colour badge, pinned to your blazer-lapel or jumper, will excite the interest and comment of all your friends!

and you will be further entitled to:
FREE ENTRY INTO THE TARGET DRAW!
All you have to do is cut off the coupon below, write on it your name and address in *block capitals,* and pin it to your letter. Twice a year, in June, and December, coupons will be drawn 'from the hat' and the winner will receive a complete year's set of TARGET books.

Write to:

TARGET BOOKS
44 Hill Street
London W1X 8LB

cut here

Full name . . . .

Address. . . . .

. . . .

. . . .

Age. . . . .

PLEASE ENCLOSE A SELF-ADDRESSED STAMPED ENVELOPE WITH YOUR
COUPON!